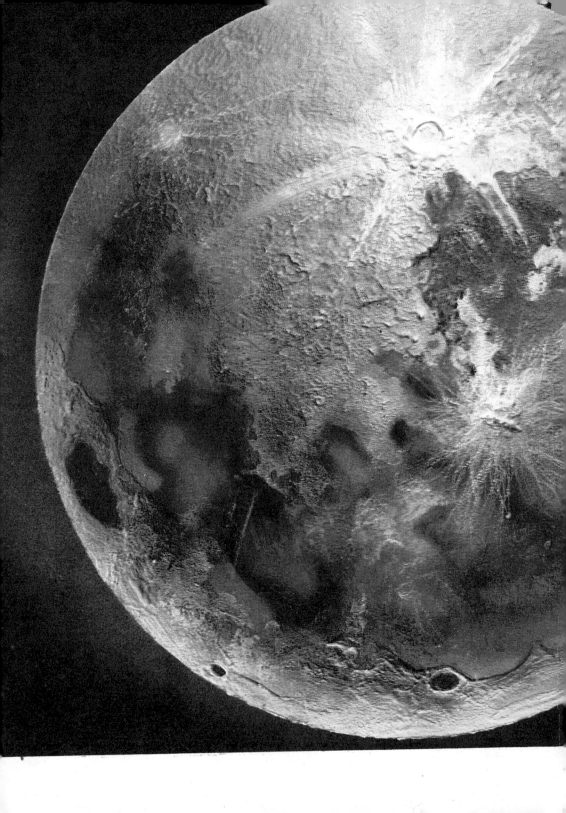

THE MOON

OUR NEIGHBORING WORLD

by OTTO BINDER

Illustrated by GEORGE SOLONEVICH

GOLDEN PRESS · NEW YORK

Third Printing, 1962

Library of Congress Catalogue Card Number 61-5450

South Pole

North Pole

OUTSTANDING MOON FEATURES

1. *Highest mountains (Leibnitz 35,000 feet).*
2. *Deepest crater (Newton, 30,000 feet).*
3. *Largest crater (Clavius, 150 miles wide).*
4. *Greatest ray system (Tycho Crater).*
5. *Brightest spot (Aristarchus Crater).*
6. *Longest mountain range (Apennines, 400 miles).*
7. *Largest "sea" (Mare Imbrium).*
8. *Greatest valley (Alpine Gorge, 80 miles).*

Most telescopes invert the moon's image, so that photographs of it are upside-down.

The Moon, Our Neighboring World

Long ago, before the era of modern astronomy, people of ancient times wove tales of magic and superstition around the moon. Even then, however, a few learned men made surprisingly accurate guesses about it. In Greece, around 400 B.C., Democritus thought it might be a round body like the earth. In 150 B.C., another Greek philosopher named Hipparchus made a remarkably close estimate of the moon's size and distance from the earth. Roman astronomers said that Luna (the Latin name for moon), was like the earth except that gods lived there instead of people.

But most people found it hard to believe that a huge body could hang in empty space. Proof did not come until 1609 when Galileo, in medieval Italy, applied the telescope. He was the first human being to look at the moon through magnifying lenses. He immediately saw its mountains, craters, plains, and other earthlike features. He also discovered four of Jupiter's largest moons and declared that they revolved around

The telescope, first used by Galileo in 1609, greatly aided study of the moon.

their mother planet, just as our moon circled around the earth.

During the 350 years since Galileo's time, the moon has been studied thoroughly. The average distance from the earth to the moon is 239,000 miles. This is not so far when you consider that many people have taken more than ten trips around the earth, whose circumference at the equator is 25,000 miles. Thus, they have covered more mileage than would be traveled on a one-way trip to the moon.

The moon's orbit is not a perfect circle but is an oval, or ellipse, so that it sometimes swings 17,000 miles closer to the earth and passes 14,000 miles further away at other times.

With a diameter of 2,163 miles, the moon is about ¼ the size of the earth. This is quite large, as moons go. Luna is the sixth largest satellite of the nine planets in our solar system. Despite its size, the weight (mass) of the moon is only 1/80 that of the earth. The moon is composed of lighter elements and probably does not have a dense iron core like the earth's. Because of this lighter mass, the moon has, at its surface, a low gravity-pull that is only 1/6 that of the earth's. A man who weighed 180 pounds on earth would weigh only 30 pounds on the moon.

The lesser gravity also makes the lunar (or moon) escape-velocity small. "Escape-velocity" means the speed any

The moon travels around the earth in an elliptical orbit to its apogee (farthest point) of 253,000 miles and perigee (nearest point) of 222,000 miles.

Weighing only 1/6 of his earth-weight on the moon, a man could leap like an acrobat, breaking all earthly Olympic records with ease.

object needs to reach in order to leave the surface of a planet or satellite. That rate of speed is 7 miles per second (25,-000 miles per hour) for an object leaving the earth, but only 1½ miles per second (5,200 miles per hour) for an object leaving the moon.

Low escape-velocity also made the moon lose its air ages ago. When air molecules are heated, they move faster. Long ago, when the moon was still hot, air molecules soon moved faster than 1½ miles a second and darted into space, lost forever. Traces of heavy gases (argon, krypton, and others) have been detected on the moon, but the total atmosphere is one trillionth that of the earth. This makes an almost complete vacuum—and a better one than scientists have been able to produce on earth. Future lunar explorers will have to bring their own oxygen.

Because it does not have an atmosphere which filters and softens heat rays, the moon scorches under the sun's intense radiations. The lunar noontime sees the thermometer reach 215 degrees Fahrenheit, just above the boiling point of water. Yet at night, with no air blanket to hold the heat, the temperature plunges way down to a frigid 250 degrees below zero.

Any water vapor that the moon once had also leaked off into space, leaving a bone-dry world. With these harsh features, the moon is thought to be a bleak planet, entirely without any form of earthlike life.

Our monthly calendar is based roughly on the time it takes the moon to revolve around the earth—27 days, 7 hours, 43 minutes. The moon only rotates on its own axis once during this time, giving it a day and a night each two weeks long.

Though the moon shows us only one face, we see somewhat more than half of it. The moon's orbit has a slight wobble (or libration) that makes it swing a bit off center, letting us see

Earthshine on the moon would be as bright as the light of 80 full moons.

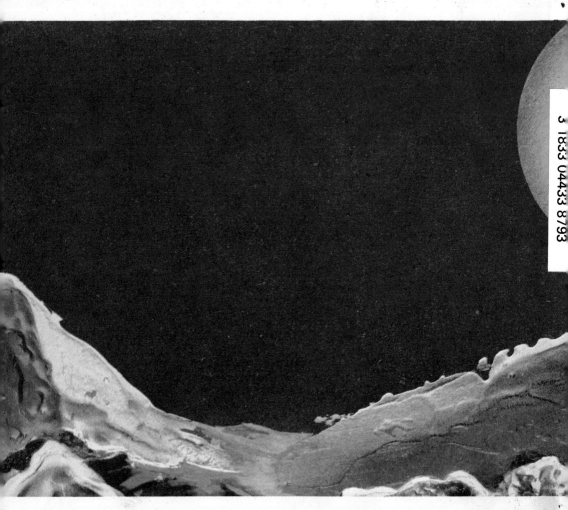

about an extra 100 miles around both sides. We see 59% of the moon's surface that way. Human eyes will see the other 41% only when spaceships from earth are able to circle around and visit the other side.

The moon, a totally dark world, radiates no light of its own and shines only because it reflects sunlight. It would take a half-million full moons to be as bright as the sun. The earth, seen from the moon, would be much more brilliant. With a surface area that is 13½ times bigger than that of the full moon, the "full earth," shining down on the moonscapes from the lunar skies, would appear to be 80 times as bright as the moon appears to us on the earth.

The moon has no light of its own but is lighted by the sun's powerful rays.

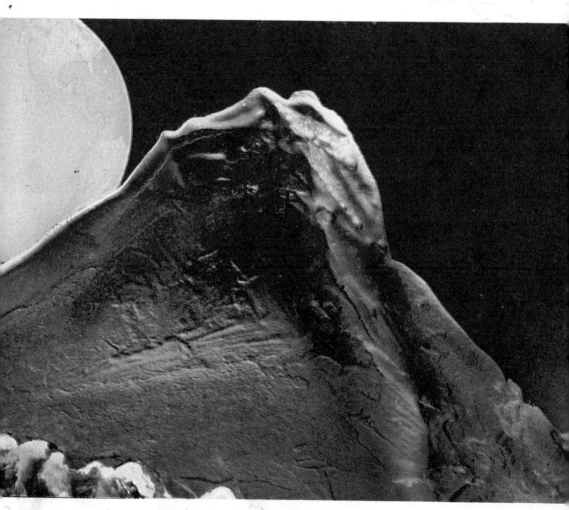

The Moon's Origin

In 1543 the Polish astronomer Nicolas Copernicus discovered that the planets of our solar system revolve around the sun, not the earth, as was formerly believed. In 1619 a German, Johann Kepler, used Copernicus' theory to figure out the orbits of the planets and moons which were known in his day.

Orbits of planets and satellites discovered later added proof that the sun was the center of the solar system.

We know now that the earth is one of nine planets whose distances from the sun range from 36 million miles (Mercury) to almost 4 billion miles (Pluto). The earth is the third one out from the

The solar system includes planets, moons, asteroids, comets, and meteors.

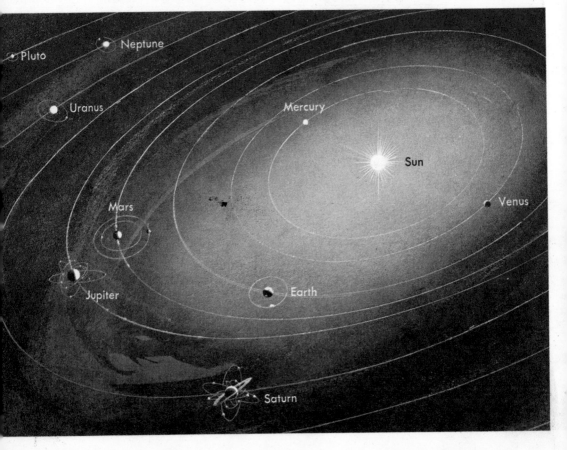

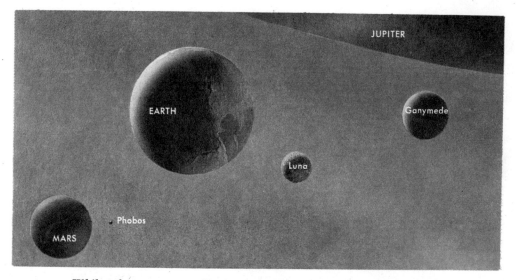

While other moons are tiny in comparison to the size of their mother planets, Luna is very large in relation to the size of the earth.

sun (93 million miles) and is the fifth largest in size.

Some of the planets, like Mercury and Venus, have no moon at all. Jupiter, on the other hand, has 12 satellites and Saturn has 9. Altogether, there are 31 moons of the 9 main planets in our solar system.

Although the earth is one of the smallest planets, its moon is one of the largest of the moons. Only five others out of the 31 are larger: Titan, with a diameter of 3500 miles; Ganymede and Callisto, each 3200 miles, Triton, 3000 miles; and Io, 2300 miles in diameter.

But all these are moons of three giant planets—Jupiter, Saturn, and Neptune —so that in comparison to the parent planets, the satellites are tiny. Ganymede, for instance, is only 1/30 the size of its mother planet, Jupiter, while our moon is more than ¼ the size of the earth.

The fact that our satellite is so large in comparison to the earth has led to a theory of how the moon was formed long ago. According to this theory, all the moons of other planets were separately formed bodies, each alongside its mother planet. But our moon was ripped out of the earth itself, according to George Darwin (son of the famous scientist, Charles Darwin). This happened, he believed, about 5 billion years ago, when the sun's powerful gravity-pull raised a "bump" on the earth's surface, which was then in a molten state.

The bump extended out further and further until it became the smaller end of a "dumbbell." Finally, the middle

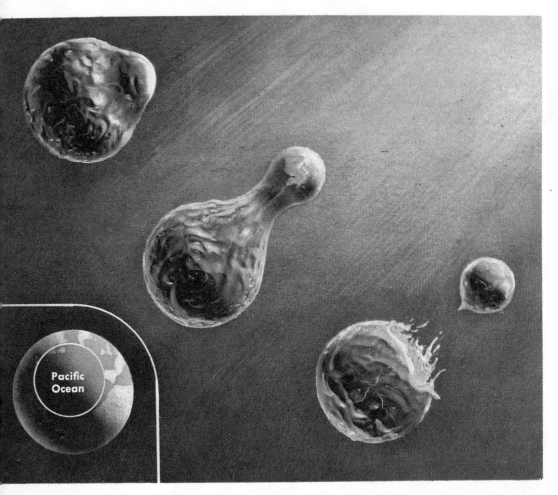

One theory suggests that the moon may have been ripped out of the earth itself eons ago.

bar stretched too thin and snapped apart. The smaller molten end of the dumbbell then whirled away free and became our moon. ·

Those who believe in this theory can point out just where the moon was ripped from the earth—in the huge hollow of the Pacific Ocean.

Other theories of the moon's birth arose. Von Weizsäcker envisioned the sun as drifting alone through space, billions of years ago. Then it floated into a huge cloud of gas and dust. Through long ages friction in the gas, along with the sun's gravity, caused the gas to contract into a disc. Then separate condensations formed, and these eventually became the planets.

A third theory, which goes back to Laplace, 150 years ago, states that the sun as well as the planets were formed from such a cloud of loose gaseous matter in space. Large masses, or bodies, gradually took shape as the gases whirled and condensed around centers of heavier matter. But only the sun, according to this concept, became molten, because its huge size created heat when its matter condensed. The planets and moons were formed "cold," or in a comparatively solid state, and gradually cooled off.

Whichever theory is right, it seems that after its formation the moon was much closer to the earth than it is now, perhaps then being only about 20,000 miles away. But the drag of earth's gravity acted as a brake that slowed down the moon's spin (rotation) and also its orbital speed of revolution. By the known laws of space motion (as in Kepler's theory), this caused the moon to recede from the earth. Mile by mile, through 5 billion years, the moon moved away until today it is 239,000 miles from the earth.

Nor has this gradual, receding process stopped. The moon is still edging away from the earth at the rate of five feet per century, so eventually it will swing 340,000 miles off.

Then, however, the gravity forces that pushed the moon and earth apart will be reversed. The moon will slowly come back all the way, and when it is within 11,000 miles, the earth's gravity will produce great strains inside the moon. It will finally shatter to bits like a world-sized bomb. Rings like those of Saturn will form around the earth from this moon debris. However, this whole process will probably take

The earth's gravitational "brake" causes the moon to steadily recede from the earth.

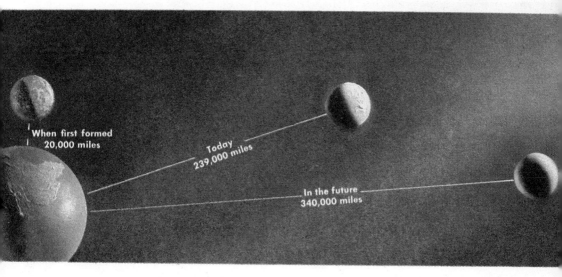

When first formed
20,000 miles

Today
239,000 miles

In the future
340,000 miles

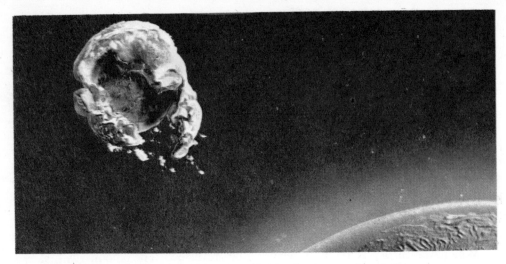

In the far distant future the moon will swing back to earth and disintegrate.

from 10 to 50 billion years to happen, a period of time almost too distant to be imagined.

For centuries to come, the moon will be in the same general place in our skies. All of human history for 12,000 years is only one tick in the cosmic clock that is measuring the vast stretch of time between the moon's ancient birth and its final death, eons in the future.

Ripped apart by gravity strains, moon particles will form earth rings.

Mapping the Moonscapes

It is strange but true that the moon has been mapped more thoroughly than some of the wild and remote regions on the earth. For almost 350 years, telescopes have scanned every mile of the moon's visible surface. Soon after the telescope was invented, moon maps were drawn. In 1651, Riccioli pub-lished a lunar map naming the craters after famous philosophers of ancient Greece, and his system is used today.

Thus, craters came to have noble names like Tycho, Plato, Aristotle, and other famous philosophers' names. Mountain ranges were simply named after earthly ones. Familiar names like

A. *Leibnitz Mts.*
B. *Straight Wall*
C. *Cordillera Mts.*
D. *Pyrennes Mts.*
E. *Carpathians*
F. *Apennines*
G. *Caucasus*
H. *Serpentine Rill*
J. *Alpine Valley*
K. *Alps*
1. *Mare Nectaris*
2. *Mare Nubium*
3. *Mare Humorum*
4. *Mare Fecunditatis*
5. *Mare Vaporum*
6. *Palus Somnii*
7. *Mare Tranquillitatis*
8. *Oceanus Procellarum*
9. *Mare Crisium*
10. *Mare Serenitatis*
11. *Lacus Somniorum*
12. *Mare Imbrium*
13. *Lacus Mortis*
14. *Mare Frigoris*
15. *Sinus Iridum*

the Alps, Apennines, Carpathians, and Caucasus Mountains are found on moon maps.

Most curious of all was the naming of the wide flat plains as *maria* (singular: *mare),* which is Latin for "seas." Early astronomers assumed that all the level areas on the moon, where no mountains existed, must be seas and oceans, as on earth. Later investigators pointed out a big flaw—no reflections of water were ever seen from those "seas." They must therefore be dry land. But the original names stuck fast and today's moon maps still show the Mare Imbrium (Sea of Showers), Lacus Mortis (Lake of Death), and the Oceanus Procellarum (Ocean of Storms).

The *maria,* which take up about half the lunar surface, are now thought to be flows of molten lava that hardened smoothly ages ago.

Thirty different *maria* have been charted on the visible portion of the moon. Of these, Mare Imbrium, which is 750 miles long, is the largest.

The entire circumference of the moon is only 6800 miles.

All the *maria* are surrounded by chains of mountain ranges that often extend unbroken for long distances. The Apennines extend 400 miles and contain 3000 peaks, some towering 18,000 feet. The average height of all mountains on the moon—12,000 feet— is remarkably high, considering the comparatively small size of the moon.

If earthly peaks were in that same proportion, they would have to reach four times higher, or up to 10 miles. Individual peaks on the moon range up to at least 30,000 feet, nearly six miles high.

All the lunar mountains, unlike those of the earth, are sharp and jagged, never rounded or smooth. This is because no air or water has ever eroded or crumbled them since they were first formed, ages ago. They throw sharp, clear shadows on the moon, which is how astronomers are able to measure their dimensions so precisely.

Great valleys also exist in the mountainous regions. The Rheita Valley, which would extend from New York City to Philadelphia, is 100 miles long, 15 miles wide, and 1500 feet deep. In proportion to the moon's size, it is as big a chasm as the Grand Canyon is on the earth.

Then there are rills (clefts), which are immense cracks in the moon's twisted surface. The Serpentine Rill,

29,000 feet

35,000 feet

over 300 miles long, starts from Herodotus Crater as a thin winding crevasse that bulges into a bigger pit, and finally widens out into a valley.

All these details of moon mapping took patient observations by many as-

19

Mount Palomar's 200-inch telescope could detect the Pentagon from the moon.

tronomers. Thousands of photographs were taken through the largest telescopes, night after night, for many years.

Less numerous, but more puzzling features of the moonscapes are the domes which look like huge, solidified bubbles. It is thought that they were formed on the molten moon long ago. Volcanic gases escaped from the interior under great pressure, forcing lava on the surface upward, to harden in a bubble or dome shape.

One of the most interesting theories about the moon is that its entire surface may be covered with a layer of fine dust. The seesawing of temperatures, from fiery daytime to sub-arctic nighttime, must expand and contract rocks violently, cracking many of them into dust. The dust layer may only be several inches deep in flat areas, but it could be miles deep in the valleys. Whether this theory is true will only be determined when spaceships are finally able to reach the moon.

Astronomers have observed that crashing meteors raise clouds of dust on the moon. The dust may come from the crumbling of rocks, caused by the extremes in the moon's temperature.

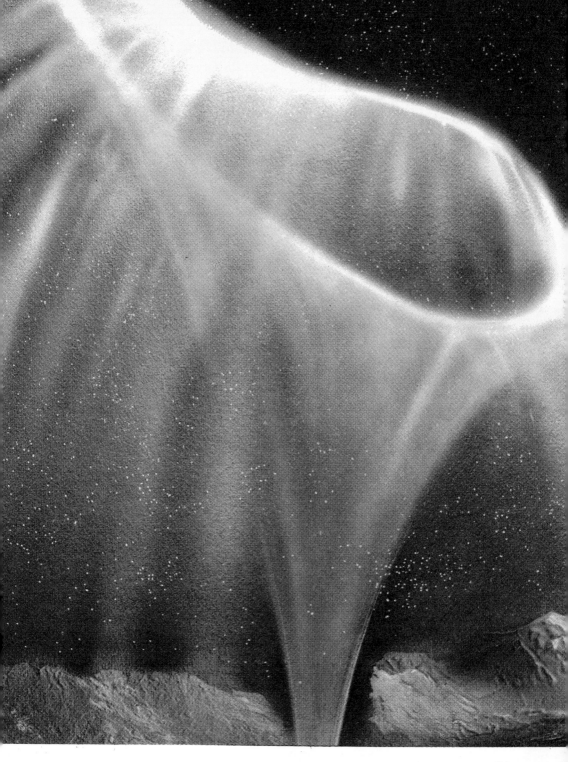

The Craters and Rays

So far, with its mountains, valleys, clefts, and waterless "seas" or plains, the moon seems similar to the earth. But one feature makes our satellite quite different from the earth—its numerous, strange craters.

An ordinary pair of binoculars clearly enables one to see the craters that are speckled all over the moon's surface. About 30,000 craters have been mapped, but it is estimated that the total number may reach 100,000 when the smaller ones are detected and labeled.

Some 600 craters have been officially named. Besides the ancient philosophers and astronomers, more recent scientists, such as Newton, Humboldt, Kepler, Encke, and Herschel, have had moon craters named in their honor.

The craters range in size from tiny holes to giant ones as large as small countries on earth. The largest is Clavius, 150 miles in diameter, which is big enough to contain the whole of Switzerland or the state of Maryland. About 150 of the craters are over 50 miles wide.

There are no comparable craters on the earth, either in size or number. Only a few dozen crater pits are known in the world. The famous Meteor Crater in Arizona, less than a mile wide, could barely be detected on the moon, even using the largest magnification of a telescope.

The moon's craters are divided into categories according to size and characteristics. The largest are the *Mountain-Walled Plains,* which are from 60 to 150 miles wide. Although their floors are not much lower than the

1. *Tycho*
2. *Clavius*
3. *Newton*
4. *Hipparchus*
5. *Theophilus*
6. *W. Humboldt*
7. *Gauss*
8. *Hercules*
9. *Atlas*
10. *Aristoteles*
11. *Cassini*
12. *Plato*
13. *Archimedes*
14. *Eratosthenes*
15. *Copernicus*
16. *Aristarchus*
17. *Herodotus*
18. *Kepler*
19. *Encke*
20. *Herschel*
21. *Grimaldi*

This map shows well-known craters that were named for famous scientists.

22

moon's general ground-level, they are ringed by tall mountain ramparts that make the craters appear as deep pits. Clavius Crater is 3 miles deep because of its encircling peaks that tower up to 17,000 feet.

The next largest, from 10 to 60 miles wide, are the *Circle Craters,* which are usually of a uniform round shape. Most of these are surrounded by mountains, too, and their floors are generally lower, making them very deep. Special features of many of the *Circle Craters,* like Tycho and Copernicus, are the solitary peaks that rise up from the center of their crater floors.

Crater Rings, 3 to 10 miles wide, have only low walls around them, or even none at all. Thousands of them pockmark the moon; but most numerous are the *Craterlets,* less than 3 miles wide, which even in big telescopes look like mere pinpricks.

Newton Crater, near the moon's south pole, is the deepest—30,000 feet from its floor to the tall peaks circling its rim. If Mount Everest were placed in the center of the crater floor, its peak would not show at all above the ramparts. Because of Newton's steep walls and its postion near the south pole, the sun rarely shines on its floor.

On the other hand, an observer in the middle of the largest shallow mountain-walled plains would not even know he was in a crater. Because the moon is small (compared to the earth), the land curves sharply and the horizon is only 2 miles away, instead of 7 miles, as it is on earth. In the center of a crater more than 100 miles wide, even the tallest peaks around the rim could not be seen 50 miles away.

There are three main theories as to how the moon's amazing craters were formed several billions years ago.

The *Volcanic Theory* states that when the moon was semi-molten long ago and just starting to cool and harden, violent eruptions broke through the thin crust. Lava spattered out, leaving pits that hardened in the form of craters. The chief objection to this theory is that although the conditions were the same for the earth, such craters

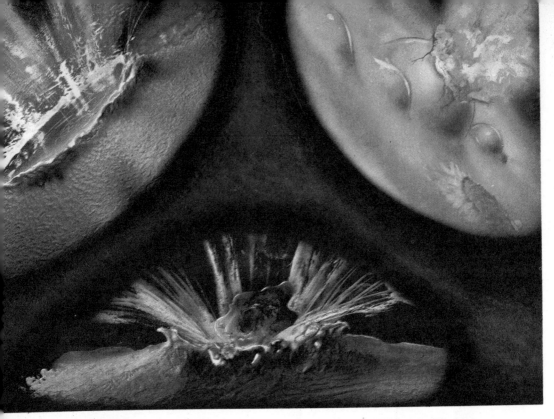

Three theories of how craters were formed are the Volcanic Theory left, *the Bubble Theory,* upper right, *and the Meteor Theory,* center.

were not formed on our molten world. Earth, being so much bigger, should have created even more gigantic craters, under the same circumstances.

According to the *Bubble Theory,* huge bubbles of gas formed domes. These burst, leaving pits behind them, the way a thick gravy or stew boils, making bubbles that burst open like tiny craters, surrounded by ramparts. But all moon craters don't have walls around them. The flaw in the Bubble Theory is that it is unable to account for the craters that are flat and rimless.

Finally, the *Meteoric Theory* says

that in ancient times many giant meteors bombarded the moon, creating the huge craters. Even if the moon was not molten, the great energy of the impact would act like an explosion, scattering the rock about. This may have happened on the earth, too, but only very recent scars, like the Arizona meteor crater, remain. Unlike the earth, the moon has no atmosphere to wear away its craters, so they all remain as rugged as ever. The bombardment is probably not finished even today, but the creation of a new crater must be a very rare event.

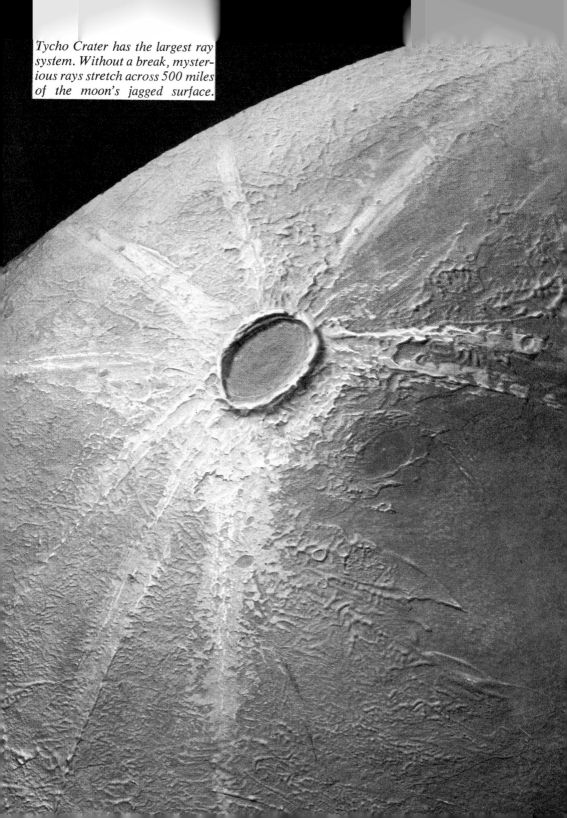

Tycho Crater has the largest ray system. Without a break, mysterious rays stretch across 500 miles of the moon's jagged surface.

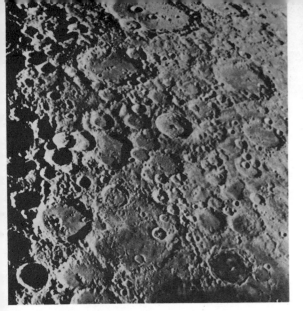

Craters are thickest near the South Pole.

Plato (see arrow) is 60 miles wide.

Craters appear rather shallow.

Chains of craters often overlap.

Right, *Telescope reveals craters in smooth "sea," Mare Imbrium. Below, one big moon crater could hold 10,000 Meteor Craters, like this one on earth.*

Alpine Gorge is 80 miles long, 3 miles deep.

Copernicus Crater has a central mountain.

Thus astronomers are divided into many camps as to the true origin of the moon's craters. This, and many other basic questions have yet to be fully explained.

Even more of a riddle are the so-called rays, bright, straight streaks radiating for long distances from a few of the craters.

Exactly what these strange, radiant markings are no one can say. They cannot be cracks in the ground, nor raised ridges, for both of those would throw shadows. The rays cast no shadow at all but look as if they are painted stripes, running for hundreds of miles across mountains, valleys, craters, and *maria*, without a break. It seems almost impossible that any marking could continue that steadily across the rough and craggy surface of the moon. The only suggestion (hardly a theory) is that the rays are some sort of whitish powder or ash which has been cast out in radiating lines. But just how this could happen nobody can guess.

Like the canals of Mars, this moon mystery may not be settled until scientists land in spaceships some day and study the rays at first hand.

Mile-wide Meteor Crater in Arizona, one of the earth's largest, would be tiny on the moon.

The faint light showing on the left side of the moon comes from sunlight which has been reflected from earth.

The Moon's Phases

Long ago, primitive tribes believed that the moon was a living creature that was slowly being "eaten up" each month, only to reappear magically whole again. That was the only way they could explain the different phases of the moon as it waned from full size to a vanishing crescent, then repeated the mysterious cycle and waxed into a full moon again.

Today, scientists know that the phases occur because the moon moves around the earth. During this revolution, the amount of its surface that can reflect sunlight onto the earth changes from less to more.

The full moon occurs each time the earth is between the moon and the sun, so that sunshine lights up the whole face turned toward us in our night sky.

If the moon did not rotate once a month, we would be able to see both sides.

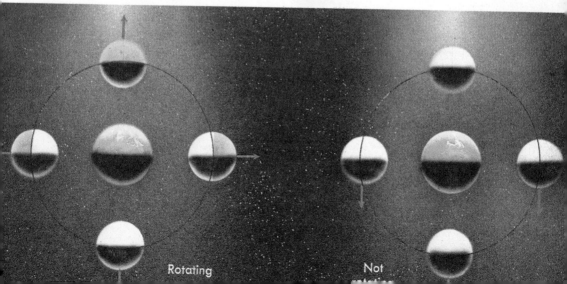

Rotating   Not

When the moon swings around and comes between the earth and the sun, only the back of the moon is lighted. Then we see no moon at all. Long ago this was named the New Moon, meaning that a new moon was being formed.

As the moon moves out of the direct line between the earth and sun, a thin crescent is lighted up for our eyes. It was called the New Moon in the Old Moon's arms, for one could still see the rest of the moon dimly, nestled in the bright, curved sliver. What lights up the rest of the moon at this time is earth-shine, or the very strong reflection of sunlight from the earth.

From the earliest times, the revolution of the moon around the earth formed a natural time-unit for mankind. The word *month* comes from *moon,* just as *Monday* is a variation of *Moon-day.*

In ancient times each month began at New Moon. But the moon goes round 12⅓ times in a year, not just 12 times, and it is too hard to make the months come out right. So the Romans, from whom we inherit our calendar, stopped using the moon as a basis for their months, and now the New Moon appears at a different time each month.

Sunlight falls on the moon and is reflected to the earth as moonlight.

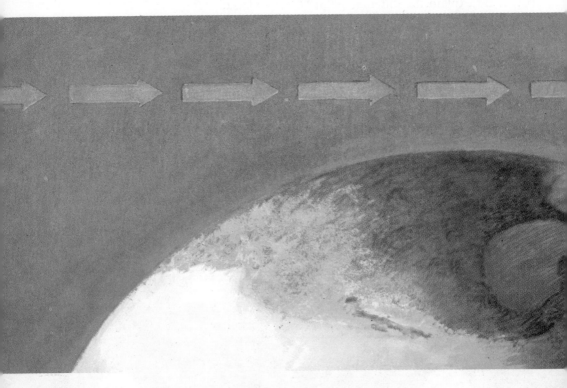

But while the moon is swinging around the earth, the earth is also orbiting around the sun. Their respective positions keep changing so that when the moon circles the earth to the same position among the stars, the sun is in a different position than before. Therefore, the moon's phase is not just the same as it was 27⅓ days before. The exact time between full moons—regardless of the moon's fixed revolution period—comes out about 29½ days, called the Synodic Period.

Every Synodic Month, year after year, the moon's phases repeat themselves as exactly as clockwork. The New Moon starts when the sun, moon, and earth—in that order—are stretched out in a straight line. Within three days, when the moon has moved part of the way around its monthly orbit, the thin crescent can be seen, and begins to grow steadily larger.

About 7½ days later, one half of the moon appears lighted, seen from the earth. This half-moon is also called the quarter-moon, meaning that one-quarter of the moon's revolution has been completed. It is called the *first* quarter, to set it apart from the half-moon that will appear later, when three-quarters of the revolution period is over.

The Synodic Period is the time between full moons, and is 29½ days.

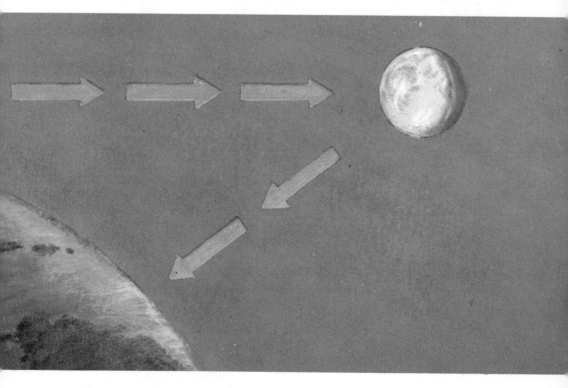

Future Husband

Horned Toad

Rabbit

AMERICAN INDIAN

IRELAND

INDI

People all over the world have "seen" different images in the moon.

In about 11 days, in the Gibbous Phase, three-quarters of the moon is shining. Almost 15 days after the New Moon, the lighted portion has expanded into the full moon.

Then the whole cycle repeats, backwards, as the moon pulls away from the sun in the race across the sky (because the moon circles the earth faster than earth goes around the sun). The Gibbous Phase, the half-moon or *last* quarter, the crescent—all repeat themselves

Woman Weaving Clouds

Goblin

Beautiful Girl

CENTRAL EUROPE

SAMOA

AMERICAN PURITAN

In Samoa, natives believed they saw an old woman weaving clouds.

in another 15 days after the full moon, bringing back the New Moon, or no moon. These two separate two-week periods are called the waxing (growing) moon and the waning (shrinking) moon, to avoid confusion.

The patterns of light and shadow on the face of the moon have been the source of many legends and optical illusions throughout history. Like visions in clouds, the markings have appeared differently to various peoples. Where we

33

say we see the Man in the Moon, the Australian Bushmen saw a cat's eye; the American Indian, a horned toad; and French peasants, the accursed face of Judas. In Ireland, they used to believe that an unmarried girl would see the face of her future husband mirrored in the moon. Even today, superstitions persist about the moon's face.

In the fall, due to certain orbital factors, the moon rises early in the evening at almost the same time, for several nights in a row. This, plus the crisp, clear autumn air, produces the most brilliant full moon of the year. It became known as the Harvest Moon long ago, for many farm folk took advantage of this bright moonlight to continue reaping their crops, late into the evening, long after the sun had set.

A superstition of old times was that a sharply tilted crescent moon, with one of its "horns" (cusps) lower than the other, meant plenty of rain was coming and that it was a good time for sowing seed. People thought that the moon looked like a full bowl being tilted by the hand of some invisible spirit which, they thought controlled the rains.

We always see the same side of the moon. The earth's gravity has gradually slowed down the moon's rotation, so that now the moon always keeps the same face turned toward us. This means that the moon rotates only once on its axis, for each revolution around the earth. Thus the lunar day and synodic month are equal—29½ days.

Moon's phases: *new moon (dark); crescent, first quarter; gibbous, full moon (15 days); gibbous, last quarter; crescent, new moon (29½ days).*

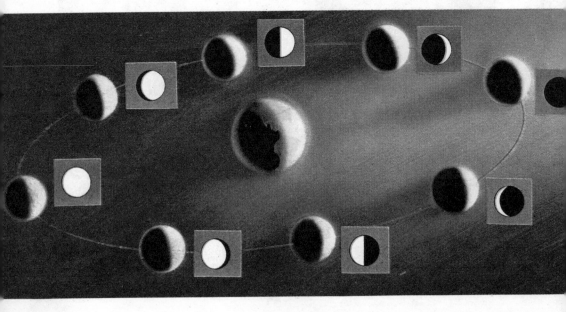

The positions of the sun, earth, and moon during both lunar and a solar eclipse.

Eclipses 1597851

Eclipses depend on the intertwined motions of three bodies—the sun, moon, and earth. The moon revolves around the earth on almost the same plane (same level in space) on which the earth circles the sun. A solar eclipse takes place whenever the moon gets between the sun and earth. A lunar eclipse happens when the earth is in the middle, between the sun and the moon.

However, the moon's orbit is slightly "tipped" five degrees from the earth-sun plane, so that the moon is often out of the direct line from the sun to the earth. Therefore, eclipses come at the irregular times when the moon is swinging from below the orbital plane to the position above.

No lunar eclipses at all occur in some years when the earth's shadow misses the moon entirely. But the moon slips in front of the sun at least twice a year. Hence, each year must have two solar eclipses.

The greatest number of eclipses, lunar and solar, that will occur in any year is seven. Only three of these can be lunar and four are solar. If there are only two lunar eclipses, five will be solar ones.

These maximum eclipse years do not occur often. The years 1917 and 1935, in this century, enjoyed seven eclipses, but this won't happen again until 1982. In most average years, however, around four or five eclipses, both lunar and solar, will take place.

A total eclipse of the sun is a memorable sight. On no other planet than earth could anyone see anything as splendid, because of a remarkable coincidence. The sun is 400 times larger than the moon and is also 400 times further away, making both globes seem to be the same size to earthly eyes. Thus, the moon exactly covers the sun's disc without cutting off from view the brilliant corona radiations around the sun's edges, which create the most dazzling eclipses possible.

A photographic time exposure shows the last stages of a lunar eclipse.

Unfortunately, the moon's long shadow comes to a point by the time it touches the earth. During a total eclipse, this shadow-tip is only 168 miles wide at the very most, usually less. Lucky people within that narrow belt enjoy the spectacle, but those on either side (for 2000 miles) can see only a partial eclipse, which is not nearly so striking. The picture on page 35 shows the paths of the sun and moon during an eclipse. Only the people standing on earth in the umbra, or small dark shadow will be able to see the total eclipse. People standing in the penumbra, or partial outer shadow, will see a partial eclipse. On the rest of the earth, where no moon shadow is cast, the eclipse will not be visible.

The path of totality (or total eclipse) races across the face of the earth at 1000 miles an hour, running ahead of the earth's rotation, and extends for about 5000 miles. The path changes with each eclipse and too often eclipses occur over the wilder regions of earth where few people live, or over long stretches of the oceans. Astronomers who wish to observe the eclipses then have to organize expeditions to faraway jungles, deserts, or islands. Since total eclipses last only a few minutes, probably not more than three living astronomers would have seen the sun in totality for more than 30 minutes if they added up all the eclipses they attended during their lifetime.

America, as a whole, is treated to an

FORECAST OF TOTAL SOLAR ECLIPSES UNTIL 1975

Date	Path of Eclipse
Feb. 15, 1961	Bay of Biscay, France, N. Italy, S.E. Europe, N.W. and N. Asia to the Arctic.
Feb. 5, 1962	Borneo, New Guinea, central and N. Pacific Ocean.
July 20, 1963	Japan, Bering Sea, Alaska, N. Canada, N. Atlantic Ocean.
May 30, 1965	S. Pacific, New Zealand, Peru.
May 20, 1966	Atlantic Ocean, NW Africa, Mediterranean, across Asia.
Nov. 12, 1966	Pacific, W. of Galapagos Is., S. South America, S. Atlantic to Indian Ocean.
Nov. 2, 1967	Antarctic Ocean, Antarctica.
Sept. 22, 1968	Arctic Ocean, N. Russia, to central Asia.
Mar. 7, 1970	Central Pacific Ocean, Mexico, Florida, to mid-N. Atlantic Ocean.
July 10, 1972	N.E. Asia, Alaska, N. Canada, to mid-Atlantic Ocean.
June 30, 1973	N. South America, Atlantic Ocean, N. Africa, to mid-Indian Ocean.
June 20, 1974	S. Indian Ocean, Antarctic Ocean, S. of Australia.

FORECAST OF TOTAL LUNAR ECLIPSES TO 1965

Date	Time	Where Visible
Aug. 25, 1961	10:08 p.m.	North and South America, W. Africa, Europe
Dec. 30, 1963	6:07 a.m.	Mid-Pacific, North America
June 24, 1964	8:07 p.m.	Africa, Europe, South America, E. North America
Dec. 18, 1964	9:35 p.m.	South America, North America, W. Africa, Europe
1965	....	(No total lunar eclipse in 1965)

FUTURE ECLIPSES VISIBLE IN THE UNITED STATES

Solar . . . (Up to 2000 A.D.)

1963, July 20	Alaska
1970, Mar. 7	Florida
1972, July 10	Alaska
1979, Feb. 26	Northwestern United States
1984, May 30	Southern United States

Lunar . . . (To 1965)

1960, Mar. 13	All of United States
1960, Sept. 5	Western United States
1961, Aug. 25	All of United States
1963, Dec. 30	Western United States
1964, June 24	Eastern United States
1964, Dec. 18	All of United States except western states.

eclipse of the sun several times a century, but the eclipse path crosses only a small area. On the average, any single locality on earth will see a total eclipse only once in 350 years. New York City is luckier, having had one in 1925 with another one scheduled in 2144, only 219 years apart.

A solar eclipse, including the partial phase, lasts about four hours altogether, starting with the first black edge of the moon cutting into the sun's disc, until the moon finally glides away again at the other side.

Before totality, while the moon covers more and more of the sun, strange

In an annular eclipse, the moon is farthest away from earth and is smaller than the sun's disc, so that a ring of sunlight is seen.

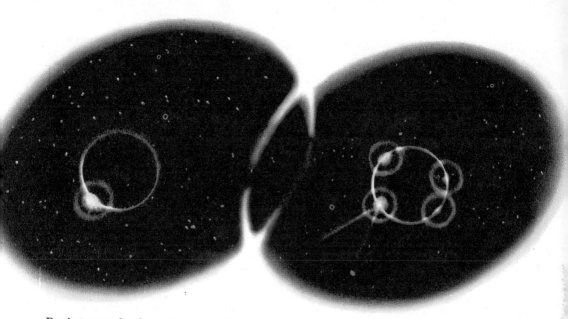

During a total solar eclipse, a "diamond ring" appears just as the sun slips behind the moon. Baily's Beads, right, are caused by sunlight flashing between lunar peaks.

shadow-bands, caused by heat-waves in the earth's atmosphere, ripple across the ground. Finally, the moon covers the last bright sliver of the sun. At the exact first moment of totality, a ring of bright sparkles, called Baily's Beads, surrounds the dark moon disc. These are flashes of sunlight that still spear between mountain peaks at the moon's rim. The spectacle is over in a moment as the sun becomes fully covered.

When the moon fully blots out the sun's disc in totality, a gloom almost as deep as night surrounds the viewers on earth. Birds are fooled into heading for their roosting places, thinking that night has already come. Strangest of all is to see the brighter stars shining in a blackish sky although it is still the middle of the day. Breathtakingly beauti-

ful is the sun's corona that now stands out, a halo of soft-colored rays that is masked at all other times by the blinding glare of the sun.

The phase of totality can last 7 minutes and 40 seconds at the very longest, but it is usually much shorter. Only twice in this century, in 1937 and 1955, did such long eclipses as those lasting over 7 minutes occur.

Lunar eclipses are much more familiar to people since everyone on one side of the earth can see them at the same time. There is no narrow path of totality on earth, within which one must be located. The earth's shadow is thrown across the moon, which is always seen by one half of the world at a time. Everybody on earth is sure to see an eclipse of the moon many times dur-

A corona, the many-colored halo, always surrounds the sun, but is masked by glare except when the solar disc is blotted out during totality.

ing his lifetime, but few people will ever see a solar eclipse. In early times, superstitious people were often frightened by the strange darkening of the moon that occurred almost every year.

A lunar eclipse is much less spectacular than that of the sun. In fact, many people may miss it if they haven't heard about it or don't look up. It begins with a gradual darkening of the bright moon as it first enters the fringes (penumbra) of the earth's shadow. It is only the core (umbra) of the shadow that finally eclipses the moon, sometimes for as long as an hour and 50 minutes.

Yet even during totality the moon can be seen as a dull coppery globe. This is due to the bending (refraction) of sunlight around the rim of the earth by its atmosphere. Thus, a certain amount of reddish sunlight penetrates the umbra-shadow and lights up the moon like a copper coin. The full span of a lunar eclipse takes about four hours to be completed.

For an observer on the moon itself, this would be an eclipse of the sun by the earth. But instead of the earth barely covering the sun's disc, it would blot out the sun entirely, like a huge black plate, also hiding its corona.

High and low tides, the changing of the level of the earth's waters, occur about every six hours.

Low Tide

The Tides

Everywhere on earth where water exists, there are tides—the alternate rising and falling of the level of the waters. Tides are caused by the pull of the moon's gravity (and to a lesser extent, by the sun's gravity) on the ocean waters. The moon's pull is stronger than the sun's because it is so much nearer to the earth.

When the moon is directly overhead, and again when it is on the opposite side of the world, the pull of lunar tides is strongest and we have high tide—the moment at which the waters reach their highest level. This rising of the water level follows the path of the moon across the sky.

Twice each day most localities have two high (flood) tides and two low (ebb) tides. It is about 6 hours between each high and low tide. However, since the moon moves in its own orbit and rises later each day, high tide is about 50½ minutes later daily.

In some places the tide may rise and fall only a foot or two, while in other areas it may vary as much as 66 feet.

41

High Tide

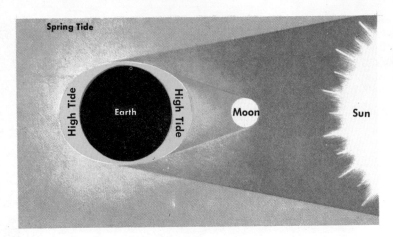

Spring Tide

High Tide   Earth   High Tide   Moon   Sun

Tides are highest at new moon and full moon, when the sun and moon pull along the same line.

Even lakes have tides, although they are small. Lake Michigan's average tide is only two inches. In the huge oceans, where much larger bodies of water can be drawn along by the moon, there are much higher tides. Those areas where the sea water funnels into narrow bays or deep canyons have the greatest tides. The Bay of Fundy, between Maine and Nova Scotia, has tides that rise and fall as much as 66 feet. The Mediterranean Sea, on the other hand, has smooth shores and shallow beaches where the difference between the high and low tides may be only 1 to 3 feet.

The earth's air also has tidal effects, but less noticeable ones than the oceans, since we live at the bottom of the at-

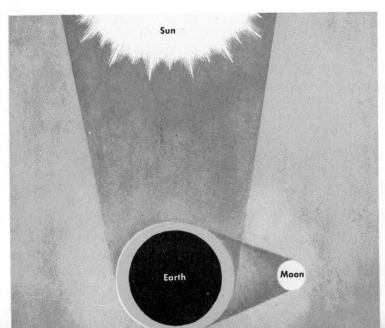

Sun

Earth   Moon

Tides are less extreme at quarter moon, when the sun and moon pull at right angles.

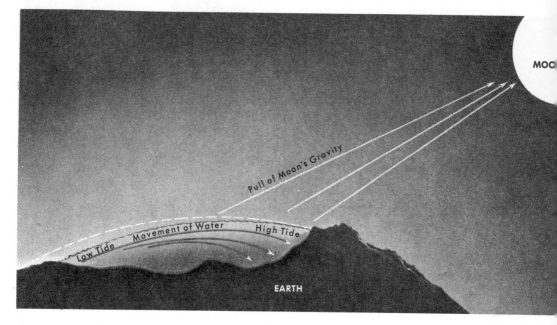

When one side of an ocean has high tide, the other shore has low tide.

mosphere, not above it, where the effects of this tide are most pronounced. Still, there is a daily advance and recession in the atmosphere.

As the moon moves swiftly across the sky, while the earth rotates under it, the high tide crests are always falling behind, not quite able to keep up with the moon. This factor acts as a steady drag or "brake" on the earth's rotation. It is a tiny force, acting on a giant planet, and only causes our day to increase an infinitesimal amount—one second each 100,000 years.

Still, those fractions of seconds pile up through long stretches of time. The day is now 1/30 of a second longer than it was in 2000 B.C. This seems like very little, but it has kept adding up for 365 days each year and 100 years each century. In the past 4000 years, the earth has "lost" seven full hours of time. Astronomers know this because ancient records of eclipses are always several hours "ahead" of what calculations show that they should have been. This is because the calculations use today's "longer" day, instead of the "shorter" day of that ancient time. The difference in the time of the eclipses shows just how much longer the day has become now.

The moon's tidal friction (or drag) will keep slowing down the earth's rotation until, in a few billion years, the earth will turn only one face to the moon, just as the moon now shows only one side to the earth.

43

How We Use the Moon

Rings around the moon foretell rain.

Primitive tribes believed that the moon was a great lamp hung in the dark sky by the Sun God when he went to rest each night. Beyond such fanciful legends, the moon actually has been useful to mankind as a huge "lantern," shedding its cheerful light. Without it, all our nights would be pitch-black, lit only by faint starlight.

We have made use of the moon in many other ways. Navigators have followed it, along with guiding stars, across the seas. In our calendar we have used the moon's monthly time-unit. During a lunar eclipse in the Middle Ages, the earth's shadow on the moon was observed to be a curve, thus giving proof that the world was round, rather than flat, as had been believed.

A more dubious use of the moon has been made by astrologers, from medieval times even up to the present day. These people professed to be able to predict the future events in a person's life by studying the position of the planets at the time of the person's birth. The position of the moon in the Zodiac, or path of the planets, promised good or evil, as the case might be. While some astronomers in the Middle Ages actually practised astrology, we know now that it is just a superstition.

Throughout the years many other superstitions have involved the moon. People have imagined that it was bad luck to see the moon at certain times,

The earth-moon system revolves around a point lying within the earth.

1,000 miles

Center of Earth
4,000 miles

44

or that crops grew best when planted at certain phases of the moon. And it was believed for a long time that Luna's rays were harmful and would strike people with madness. We know today that all these beliefs are wrong, but we still use the word *lunacy* (insanity).

Many moon superstitions concern the weather. People once thought they could tell whether it would rain by seeing whether the new crescent moon was level and would "hold water" or whether it was steeply tilted so that the water would spill out. But we now know that the tilt of the crescent simply depends on the time of year. One other old superstition has some truth in it, though. A ring around the moon often does foretell rain, because the thin clouds that cause the ring often come just before a change in the weather.

In modern times, the moon has been important to scientists in making many calculations and studies. Until the recent development of the coronograph, the only time that the sun's corona could be seen was when the moon caused total eclipses. But the faint outer parts of the corona can still be seen only during a total eclipse.

Astronomers have also used the time of total eclipses to look for new planets between the sun and Mercury. Many careful searches have failed to find any, and Mercury remains, so far as we know, the closest planet to the sun.

Einstein's theory of bent light rays was partly proved by a solar eclipse.

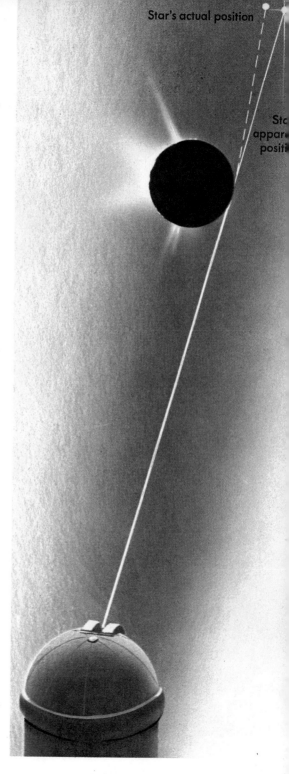

Star's actual position

Star's apparent position

Some calendar dates, like Easter, depend on the moon's phases.

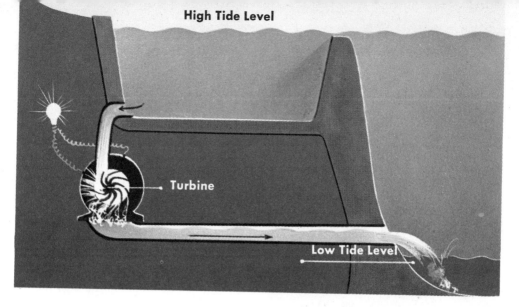

Powerful earth tides run turbines at coastal tide-water stations.

The solar eclipse of 1919 partially proved Einstein's theory of relativity. Einstein had said that the sun's gravity could bend a star's light-rays. This could only be observed when the moon's disc blotted out the sun's glare, allowing nearby stars to be seen close to the edge of the sun. Sure enough, careful measurements showed that stars near the rim of the sun seemed to have changed their positions slightly. This proved, as Einstein predicted, that the starlight had been bent around the sun.

We also owe other scientific measurements to the moon. As the moon travels around the earth each month, it often passes in front of stars and hides them for an hour or so. The disappearance of a star behind the moon is called an *occultation*. When a star is occulted by the moon, it disappears instantly. This shows that the moon has no atmosphere to speak of, for a layer of air around the moon would cause the star to wink out more slowly. A very few stars, though, disappear a shade more slowly than others, showing that they are large stars and that the edge of the moon takes a little longer to cover them.

Astronomers also use occultations to measure time and position very accurately. They can calculate the location of the moon so closely that observing occultations is a way of telling time. These observations are so precise that they can check on the rotation of the earth. Also, when two astronomers in different parts of the earth watch the moon occult the same star, their observations can be used to map the earth more accurately.

Down on earth itself, the moon gives us a certain amount of electrical power that comes from huge tidal stations

47

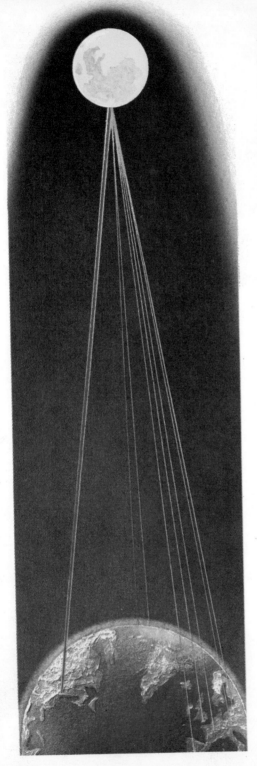

which are built along seacoasts with exceptionally high tides. As the moon's gravity creates high tide, it literally "lifts" millions of tons of water as high as 25 or 50 feet into storage tanks. At low tide the tanks are opened and the water runs down, like a miniature Niagara Falls, to spin turbines and generate electricity. Twice a day, endlessly, the moon does its part in making the tide-power station work.

A brand-new and vitally important use of the moon stems from an experiment made in 1947, when radar waves were bounced off the moon for the first time by American scientists. A short time ago they also succeeded in bouncing messages off the moon.

This will improve world-wide short-wave radio communication, which previously bounced signals from the ionosphere 60 miles above earth. But the ionosphere, a layer of electrified particles, is tricky and unreliable, sometimes causing loud static or fading signals. This has often cut off distress calls from ships at sea.

But if short waves are beamed into space, the moon will never fail to bounce the signals back. Even if clouds hide the moon, the waves can go through and find their target. Since one-half of the earth is always under the moon, the return signals can be picked up at any point around the world for 12,500 miles.

Radio waves bounced from the moon can reach many of our cities at the same time.

Target, the Moon

On October 11, 1958, the U.S. Air Force sent *Pioneer I,* a 40-pound missile, a distance of 72,000 miles, or almost one-third of the way to the moon. The Army's 13-pound *Pioneer III,* on December 6, 1958, went 65,000 miles before falling back and burning up in the earth's atmosphere. Though it failed, America tried first to reach the vicinity of the moon. Russia succeeded when it launched its *Lunik* on January 2, 1959, with a payload of 800 pounds. Less than two days later, *Lunik* sailed past the moon at a distance of less than 5000 miles. It kept going, to become a small new planet of the sun, never to return to earth.

Then on October 7, 1959, a Russian moon probe succeeded in photographing the back side of the moon.

Other unmanned missiles will be shot at the moon. All of these lunar probes will be based on the unchanging laws of motion in space. Any missile must achieve a speed of at least 24,900 miles an hour in order to break free of the earth's powerful gravitational pull.

Then a missile that not only lands on the moon, but leaves again under its own power, will be able to return to the earth. This will call for more rocket fuel to overcome the moon's escape-velocity (5200 miles per hour).

Then, after the unmanned missiles have paved the way, a manned rocket or spaceship will reach the moon. No one can say exactly when this day will come. Estimates range from as early as 1965 to the end of this century. If it is the earlier date, then some young boys who are living today are destined to become the first men on the moon. The moonship will be ready by the time they reach manhood and are trained for the great venture.

When the first moon explorers step out of their ship in protective spacesuits, they will see around them a bleak, alien world totally unlike the earth. The lack of both air and water means that there

Three moon-missile orbits: to strike, to return, or to circle the moon.

can be no winds, no rain, or rainbows, no lightning storms or thunder, no clouds or humidity—nor any weather at all. There will be only intense heat above the boiling point of water in the daytime, and at night, an iciness twice as bitter as the South Pole.

As only air can carry sound waves, utter silence will surround the moon visitors. If they were to drop a feather, it would fall like a stone. Feathers can float only in buoyant air.

Metals would not tarnish on the moon for centuries as there would be no oxygen or water to rust them. Fresh foods would keep indefinitely without spoiling since there are no living bacteria on the moon to cause decay.

When men explore the whole moon they will not have so much to explore as on the earth. The total lunar surface, including the side that we never see, is 12 million square miles, or about the size of Africa. The moon's low gravity-pull (1/6 of the earth's) will allow the men to travel by leaping 100 feet at a bound, like huge frogs. Even with heavy spacesuits, they will weigh less than half their earthly weight.

In the daytime sky—which is always black, with no atmosphere to scatter sunlight—the sun's corona and the stars will be seen at all times. The full-earth will be a big greenish globe with the continents and oceans clearly visible except when under cloud packs. Tele-

Moon probes are sent aloft by such missiles as the Air Force's Thor.

Reaching the moon by spaceships, future space explorers will find a strange bleak world, lighted at night by brilliant earthshine.

scopes would easily pick out the Great China Wall, the Grand Canyon, and even the glow of large cities at night.

Meteors will be a constant hazard on the moon. Not burning up as they do in earth's blanket of air, millions of meteors rain down on the moon's surface day and night. They travel so fast that even a tiny one would blow a hole in a spacesuit. And occasionally a meteor as large as a marble or a baseball would come crashing down at a speed as high as 45 miles per second. Such a meteor could destroy a building or a spaceship. Fortunately, large meteors are rare.

In spite of its harsh living conditions, the moon may some day have human colonists. Scientists speak of cities nestled within craters, covered by plastic domes and comfortably air-conditioned.

Adventurous men may want to use the moon for several good reasons. The moon would be the ideal spaceport for all interplanetary travel. Rocket ships could take off and land much more easily in the moon's low field of gravity than under the earth's strong pull.

Astronomers on the moon would find perfect viewing conditions through the crystal clear space vacuum that touches the lunar surface. The stars and planets would appear brighter and sharper. Clear-cut photographs taken from the moon would probably prove or disprove the rumored Martian canals even before ships went to Mars.

Prospecting on the moon may also attract earthmen if valuable minerals or precious jewels are discovered. But first we will have to find a way to bring things back from the moon cheaply.

Cities of the moon are a far look into the misty future. Yet, even such a possibility as this may sometime occur.

radar
for
meteor
detection

lunar alps

lunar
science labor

sealed
housing
for
personnel

52

full earth

ont Blanc

power lines from solar dynamo

Silicon-cell carpet (black to absorb sunlight) converts sun-energy to electricity.

sun-power station

edge of Mare Frigoris

transportation by sealed tractor

FIRST HUMAN OUTPOST ON THE MOON

53

Index

PICTURE CREDITS: Photographs from Lick Observatory, pp. 6, 17, 18, 26 (top left), 27 (top right and bot. left), 46; Mount Wilson and Palomar Observatories, pp. 26 (top right and bot. left and right), 27 (bot. right); Arizona State Travel Commission, p. 27 (top left), 28; American Museum of Natural History, pp. 36, 38; U.S. Air Force, p. 50.

Pictures on pp. 30-31, 41, by John Polgreen; p. 42, by James Gordon Irving.

C